THE LABORS OF HERCULES

Long ago in Greece, when the world was young, there lived a very strong man. His name was Hercules. Even as a baby, Hercules was brave and strong. When Hercules grew up he met a wise woman who told him that he must do twelve great deeds. She said if he did them well he would go to live with the gods on Mount Olympus.

This is the easy-to-read story of Hercules, and the twelve labors he performed to become a god on Mount Olympus.

Other SEE AND READ
Beginning to Read Storybooks

A SEE AND READ
Beginning to Read Storybook

THE LABORS OF
HERCULES

by Paul Hollander

Illustrated by Judith Ann Lawrence

G. P. Putnam's Sons   New York

To Mike Guinzburg

Library of Congress Catalog Card Number: 65-13319

Published simultaneously in the Dominion of Canada by
Longmans Canada Limited, Toronto
07209

Long ago, when the world was
young, there lived a very strong man
in the land of Greece. His name was
Hercules. His mother was a woman
called Alcmene, and his father was
the god Zeus.

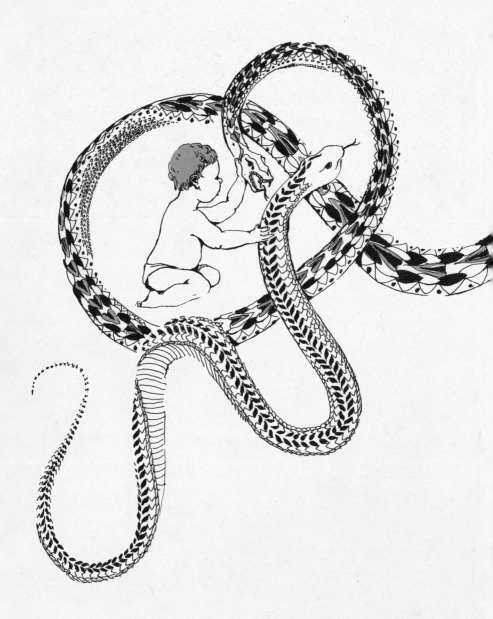

Even when he was a baby, Hercules was brave and strong. One day two great snakes came into the room where little Hercules was sleeping. He woke up and caught the snakes in his hands and killed them. He was only ten months old then!

The next day, Alcmene told a wise old man about Hercules and the snakes. The old man said, "He will be a very great hero. He will do wonderful things. One day he will go to the home of the gods and live with them."

The boy Hercules grew up and became the strongest man in Greece.
He could shoot an arrow farther than
anybody else. He could box and wres-
tle; he could run and swim. Although
he was so strong, he was kind and
friendly. He tried never to harm anybody.

When Hercules grew up, he met a woman who was very wise. She told him, "You must go to work for your cousin, King Eurystheus. For twelve years you must do everything he tells you to do. If you work for him well, you will go to the home of the gods to live."

So Hercules went to King Eurystheus. The cowardly king was afraid of his strong cousin. He did not want Hercules to stay with him.

Hercules said, "I must work for you. The wise woman said I must."

Eurystheus wanted to get rid of Hercules. So he made up many hard tasks for Hercules. He told Hercules to do things that nobody had ever done.

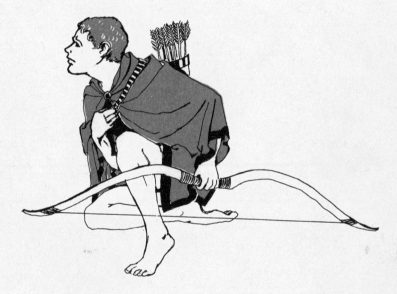

"First," Eurystheus said, "you must kill the Lion of Nemea."

This was a lion that lived near a town named Nemea. All the people of Nemea were afraid of it. It killed cows and sheep, and sometimes it killed men and women, too. The lion's skin was so strong that no arrow could hurt it.

Hercules went into the forest and pulled up a tree. He made a club out of the tree. It was so heavy no other man could carry it. Then he went looking for the lion.

He shot arrows at it. But even the arrows of the mighty Hercules did no harm. Then the lion jumped at Hercules.

Hercules hit it with his big club, and the lion stopped. Hercules killed it with his hands alone.

He took the skin of the lion and made a coat for himself. When he came back to King Eurystheus, he was wearing the lion's skin. It looked as if the lion itself was coming to see the king!

The cowardly king next sent Hercules to kill a monster. It was called the Hydra. The Hydra was a kind of snake with nine heads. It was very dangerous because of its poison. Hercules and his friend Iolaus went to the place where the Hydra lived.

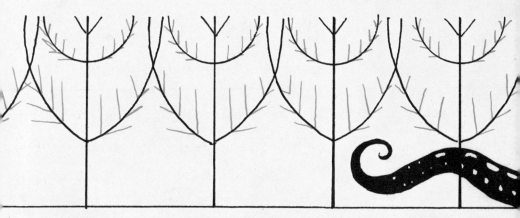

The Hydra came out to meet them. It was hissing and wanted to bite.

Hercules tried to cut off the monster's heads with a sword. Every time he cut a head off, two new ones grew

in its place! But Hercules knew a way.
"Light a fire," he told Iolaus.

Now each time Hercules cut off a
head of the Hydra, Iolaus would burn
the place where the head had been.

That way no new heads would grow. Soon the Hydra was dead. All of its heads were cut off.

Hercules put the Hydra's blood on his arrows. From now on the arrows had poison on them. They would kill anything they hit.

Eurystheus was surprised that Hercules had killed the Hydra. He thought the Hydra would have killed Hercules. But he still had plenty of work for Hercules to do.

Now he sent Hercules into the
mountains to catch a famous deer.
The deer belonged to Diana, the goddess of hunting.

It would have been easy for Hercules to kill the deer with his poisoned
arrows. But Eurystheus did not want
him to do that.

"Bring the deer to me alive," the king said.

For a whole year Hercules lived in the forest. He ran after the wonderful deer. The deer had horns of gold and hoofs of brass. Hercules ran after the deer over river and hill. At last the deer was so tired it could run no more.

Hercules took it and put it over his back. He was going to carry it to King Eurystheus. Then the beautiful goddess Diana came out of the forest.

"You must not harm my deer," she said.

"I am taking it to Eurystheus," Hercules answered. "After he sees it I will bring it back to you. I will not harm it at all."

Diana let him have the deer. Hercules showed it to his cousin. Then he brought it back to Diana's forest.

Now Eurystheus sent busy Hercules to catch another wild animal. This was a wild pig that made everyone afraid. It had big sharp teeth and bright yellow eyes. Hercules caught the pig and took it to Eurystheus. King Eurystheus was so afraid, he jumped into a big pot to hide. Hercules saw this and laughed. He made believe he had not seen Eurystheus hide.

"This pot will be a good place to

keep the pig," Hercules said. And he put the pig into the giant pot!

Eurystheus was very surprised.

He cried out because he was afraid. But the pig was afraid, too. It did not hurt him.

Soon Hercules had a new task to do.

He had to clean out the stables of King Augeas, who was a friend of Eurystheus. Augeas had many, many cows and sheep. The stables had not been cleaned in ten years. A great river was near them. Hercules dug a ditch and made the river run into it. The water of the river ran right through the stables of Augeas!

In one day all the dirt was washed away. The stables looked bright and clean. It was one of the easiest of the tasks of Hercules. He had only made a river take a new path. It was easy — for him!

Now once more he had to drive away monsters. He had to kill the birds that lived around the lake of Stymphalus.

They were strange birds with claws and beaks of iron. They carried off sheep and cows and little children.

Hercules could not fight with the birds while they were in the water. But he tricked them. He rang a loud bell. The birds flew into the air to see who was making the noise.

33

Hercules shot them, one by one, with his poisoned arrows. He killed all the monster birds and made the lake safe for ducks and geese.

Hercules next had to go over the sea to the island of Crete. A huge bull was running wild there. It was as white as snow and its horns were as bright as silver. The bull was beautiful but dangerous. No one could catch it.

Hercules found the bull and wrestled with it. He caught it by the horns and made it lie down. The bull saw how strong Hercules was. It became gentle as a lamb.

Hercules took the bull to Eurystheus. The bull swam across the sea and Hercules rode on its back!

Eurystheus did not let brave Hercules rest. He sent him north to the land of Thrace. Diomedes was king there. Diomedes was a cruel man who was not good to his people. He had two warhorses so strong they had to be kept in chains. Some said that the horses of Diomedes ate men and women!

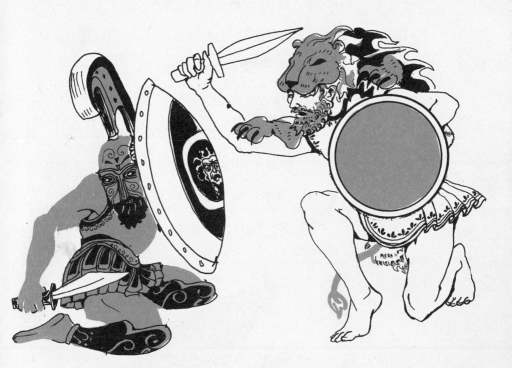

Hercules had a fight with Diomedes and made him a prisoner. Then he took the horses back to Eurystheus. But the cowardly king was afraid to keep them. He set them free and they ran off into the hills. The god Zeus sent wolves to kill the wild horses.

Next Hercules went to the land of the Amazons. Eurystheus wanted him to bring back the belt of Hippolyte, Queen of the Amazons. The Amazons were women as strong as men. They liked hunting and making war. The belt was of gold and jewels. Hercules took the wonderful belt from the Amazon queen. First he had to fight long and hard with the strong woman.

For his next task Hercules had to go far away. He had to go to an island past the place where the sun sets. Eurystheus told him to bring back the red cows of the giant Geryon.

Geryon was a great monster. He had three heads and six legs and two wings.

It took Hercules a long time to reach Geryon's island. He went over rivers and mountains. He went into a desert where there was no water to drink. Then he came to the sea. Apollo, the god of the Sun, helped him. Apollo sent Hercules a magic boat made of gold. Hercules went to Geryon's island. He climbed a high mountain to look for the cows.

Then Geryon came. He held six clubs at a time, one in each of his six hands! But Hercules shot a poisoned arrow that killed the giant.

Then he put the cows of Geryon into the magic boat and sailed away from the island. On the way back to Greece many of the cows were taken by robbers. But Hercules brought most of the cows back for King Eurystheus.

Right away, Hercules had to go to
a far land again. This time, the greedy
king wanted three golden apples that
grew in a wonderful garden.

No one quite knew where the garden was, though. Hercules asked
everyone.

He came to a river where lovely girls were swimming.

"Do you know where the garden of the golden apples is?" he asked them.

"No," one of them said. "But there is an old man named Nereus who knows almost everything. Catch him and he will tell you how to get the golden apples."

Soon Nereus came along. He lived in the sea, and his hair looked liked seaweed. Hercules caught the old man and held him. Nereus changed his shape, trying to get away. He turned into a deer and then into a bird and then into a dog. Still Hercules held him.

"What do you want?" Nereus said at last.

"I want to know how to find the three golden apples," Hercules said.

Nereus told him to go to Africa. There he would find a giant named Atlas, whose job it was to hold up the sky. Atlas would get the golden apples for Hercules.

Hercules looked for Atlas. He found the giant, who looked very tired. Atlas had been holding up the sky since the world began.

"Will you get me the golden apples?" Hercules asked.

"Yes, I will," said Atlas. "But you must hold up the sky for me while I get them!"

So Hercules put his shoulder to the sky. Atlas went to get the golden apples. Soon he came back with them. But the giant laughed. "I am tired of holding up the sky," he told Hercules. "Now *you* will hold it up forever!"

"All right," said Hercules, "I will hold the sky. But you take it, just for a minute. Let me put a pad on my shoulder, so it will be easier for me."

"Very well," Atlas said. "But only for a minute!"

And he took the sky back from Hercules. As soon as Atlas was holding up the sky again, Hercules said good-bye and began to leave.

"Come back!" Atlas cried. "Come back and take the sky from me!"

But Hercules only laughed, and went away with the golden apples.

One more task had to be done. Eurystheus sent him into the dark world of dead people. Hercules had to bring back the three-headed dog Cerberus. Cerberus watched the gate to the land of the dead.

Hercules went down into the dark world. He went right to Pluto, the god of the dead.

"Eurystheus wants me to take your dog Cerberus," Hercules said.

"You may take him," Pluto answered, "but only if you can catch him with your hands alone. You may not use your club or your arrows."

Hercules thanked Pluto. Then he went looking for Cerberus. The dog barked with its three mouths. But it was not as strong as mighty Hercules.

Hercules picked the dog up and held it high over his head. He took it back to the other world and showed it to Eurystheus.

"Go away," Eurystheus said. "Take the dog back to Pluto. Never come here again. I am afraid of you, Hercules. I have no more work for you!"

So Hercules gave Cerberus back. Now he was a free man. He had done twelve great tasks for Eurystheus. People everywhere in the world knew of Hercules.

He did many more great things.
Then when it was time for Hercules
to die, the words of the wise man
came true. Hercules did not go to the
dark world of dead people. The gods

took him up to their home on top of
Mount Olympus. He became a god
himself. He went to live with his
father, Zeus. He lived with the shining
sun god Apollo and the goddess Diana
and all the other gods.

The people of Greece still talk about Hercules and the wonderful things he did long ago. They will never forget what he did when he was a man and lived in the world.

Guide to Pronunciation

Alcmene	alk-MEE-nee
Amazons	AM-a-zons
Apollo	a-POL-o
Atlas	AT-las
Augeas	AW-jee-as
Cerberus	SER-ber-us
Crete	KREET
Diana	die-AN-a
Diomedes	die-OM-eh-dees
Eurystheus	you-RIS-thee-us
Geryon	JERRY-on
Hercules	HERK-you-lees
Hippolyte	hi-POL-i-tee
Hydra	HIGH-dra
Iolaus	eye-o-LAY-us
Nemea	NEE-mee-a
Nereus	NEHR-ee-us
Olympus	oh-LIM-pus
Pluto	PLOO-toe
Stymphalus	stim-FAIL-us
Zeus	ZOOSE

KEY WORDS

arrow(s)	goddess	prisoner
beak(s)	gold (golden)	robber(s)
belt	greedy	seaweed
brass	harm	shoulder
brave	hero	skin
bull	hiss(ing)	smart(er)
chain(s)	hoof (hooves)	snake(s)
claw(s)	horn(s)	stable(s)
club	hunt(ing)	strong(est)
cousin	jewel(s)	task(s)
cowardly	magic	warhorse(s)
cruel	monster(s)	wise
gentle	path	wolf (wolves)
giant	poison(ed)	wrestle
god(s)		

The Author

PAUL HOLLANDER has been a full-time free-lance writer since he graduated from Columbia University in 1956. Originally specializing in science fiction, Mr. Hollander currently writes nonfiction paperback originals as well as books for young people. He, his wife, and their three cats live in Riverdale, New York.

The Artist

JUDITH ANN LAWRENCE was graduated from Columbia University with a B.F.A. and has taught art, been a social worker and a secretary. Since then she has become a full-time free-lance illustrator. She has a number of juveniles to her credit including *1066, Johnny Appleseed,* and *Home of the Red Man.* The artist lives in Manhattan with her writer husband, James Blish, and two cats.